EVOLUTION
COLOURING AND ACTIVITY BOOK

Designed and illustrated by

Sabina Radeva & Iglika Kodjakova

PUFFIN

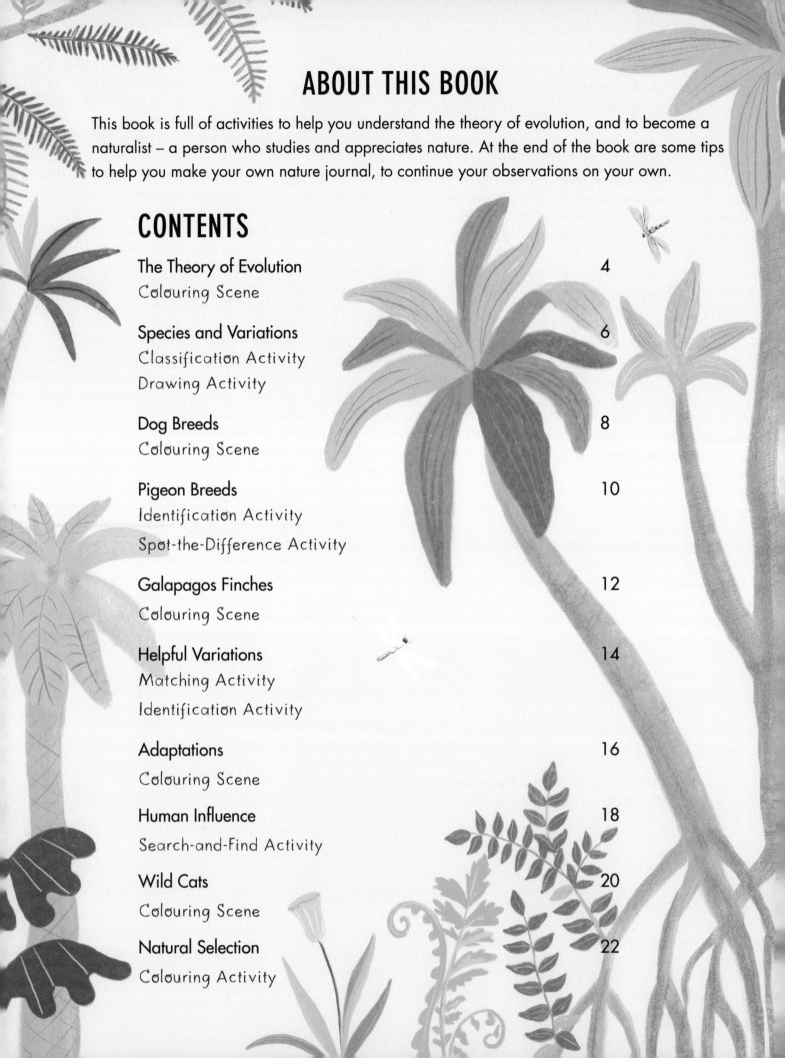

ABOUT THIS BOOK

This book is full of activities to help you understand the theory of evolution, and to become a naturalist – a person who studies and appreciates nature. At the end of the book are some tips to help you make your own nature journal, to continue your observations on your own.

CONTENTS

THE THEORY OF EVOLUTION

The theory of evolution explains how all living organisms have changed, and new species have formed over millions of years, throughout the history of life on Planet Earth.

In the picture below, you can see how living things used to look millions of years ago. Some looked quite different from plants and animals today. We no longer have dinosaurs like Tyrannosaurus, Velociraptor or Triceratops around (they went extinct about 65 million years ago), but we still have birds! Modern birds evolved from a group of small two-legged dinosaurs known as theropods.

Can you name one famous member of the theropod family, a scary predator that weighed more than eight tons and measured up to 12 metres (40 ft) long?

SPECIES AND VARIATIONS

Scientists study lots and lots of living things. There are many different organisms on Earth and scientists like to organize them into groups. For example, they can organize or classify animals and plants based on how they look, where they live and what they eat.

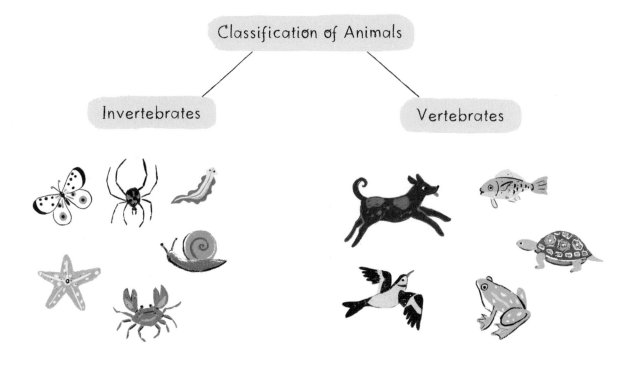

 Organize in Groups

Look at the three pictures below. Which of these two animals are most similar and belong in the same group? Can you identify which of these are insects and which is a mammal?

Butterfly

Melanargia galathea

Cat

Felis catus

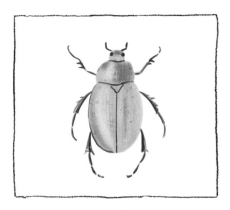

Beetle

Cotalpa lanigera

The term **species** often refers to a group of similar-looking living things that are able to reproduce and have offspring together. Even though animals of the same species can look very similar, they also have differences, called **variations**.

 Art Variations

1. Grab pencils, crayons and a blank sheet of paper.
2. Now, draw a lizard by looking at the pictures below.
3. Next, take a new sheet of paper and draw the same lizard again.
4. Repeat this as many times as you like, using a new sheet of paper each time.

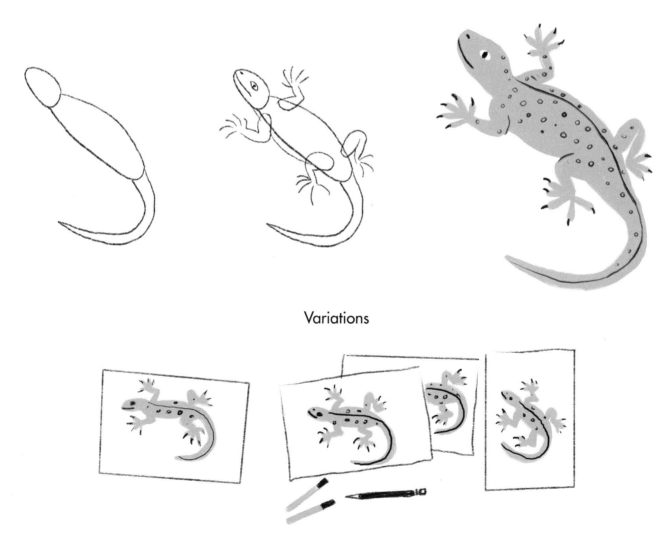

Variations

Compare your pictures of lizards. They all have small differences, don't they?
Similarly, no two animals in nature are identical, even when they belong to the same species.

DOG BREEDS

You probably know lots of dogs of various sizes and colours, but even tiny dogs, tall dogs and big soft fluffy dogs all belong to the same species!

PIGEON BREEDS

Pigeons of different breeds can look very different when compared with one another, but they all belong to the same species.

✏️ In the picture below, can you circle all the birds that are pigeons?

1. *Jacobin;* 2. *Rose-breasted cockatoo;* 3. *Emperor penguin;* 4. *Pouter;* 5. *Barb pigeon;* 6. *Nun pigeon;* 7. *Grey parrot;*

8. *Common ostrich;* 9. *Rock dove;* 10. *Stork;* 11. *Toco toucan;* 12. *Golden eagle;* 13. *Burrowing owl;* 14. *Fantail;*

15. *Tumbler;* 16. *Mallard duck*

SPOT THE SUBTLE DIFFERENCES

Take a good look at the finches in the picture below.

 Can you circle all the finches that are identical to the ones in the square?

a.

b.

c.

d.

e.

f.

g.

h.

i.

j.

k.

l.

m.

n.

o.

p.

q.

r.

s.

t.

GALAPAGOS FINCHES

Galapagos finches have evolved beaks in all sorts of shapes and sizes.
These differences help them to pick up their favourite snacks.

Different beaks are suitable
for different nibbles.

Some finches, for example, have long and sharp beaks to tear cactus flowers and others have short beaks and feed on seeds.

HELPFUL VARIATIONS

As we saw earlier, individuals from the same species each have small differences.
Some of these differences (or variations) can work to the animal's advantage,
helping it to survive in the wild, to hide or hunt, or to have more babies.

 Compare and Match

In the picture below there is a group of giraffes with necks of different lengths.
Can you match each giraffe to the tallest plant it can eat?

Now, imagine that the plants A, B and C are all eaten, and only the tallest trees are left.
Which giraffe will still be able to reach their food and thrive? Which has the most helpful
variation in their new environment?

 Q: Why do giraffes have long necks?
A: So they can't smell their stinky feet.

Camouflage

Some insects have evolved body shapes and colours to help them hide in their natural habitat.

For each of the habitats below, find the insect that best matches it, or blends in, allowing it to hide from predators or to hunt. Then write the number of the habitat next to the bug. The first one has been done for you.

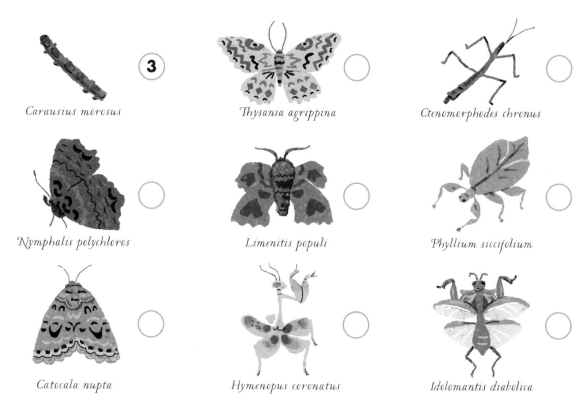

Carausius morosus   3

Thysania agrippina

Ctenomorphodes chronus

Nymphalis polychloros

Limenitis populi

Phyllium siccifolium

Catocala nupta

Hymenopus coronatus

Idolomantis diabolica

15

ADAPTATIONS

Snakes are well adapted to their environment. With no legs or arms, snakes can slither through grass, water or stones without causing a disturbance that might frighten their prey. Their colours help them blend into their environment and prevent predators from noticing them.

HUMAN INFLUENCE

The peppered moth has two variations – one is pale and the other is dark. The dark variety of peppered moth became more common between 1811 and 1848, because it blended in better with the nearby trees, which had been blackened by chimney smoke and pollution.

PALE

Biston betularia typica

DARK

Biston betularia carbonaria

✏️ Find All the Moths

Blending in with the trees is important for moths to avoid being spotted and eaten by birds. Find all the peppered moths in the picture on the right. Which ones are easier to spot and why?

Number of moths: _____

WILD CATS

Different animals use different types of camouflage for their particular environment.
For example, many animals that live in jungles or savannahs have stripes or spots.
This is a disruptive pattern, which makes them difficult to see among lots of long grass or tall
shrubs. Colour these wild cats with the right kind of camouflage for their environment.

Q: Why do tigers have stripes?
A: So they don't get spotted.

NATURAL SELECTION

Natural selection occurs when a particular characteristic makes some organisms better adapted to their surroundings, giving them an advantage that helps them to survive and reproduce more successfully than other individuals — they may live longer, have more babies and increase in numbers! These helpful characteristics are then passed down from the parents to their offspring.

A

Frog Pond

In a small pond lived two varieties of frogs – light green and dark green. The hungry storks could spot one of those colours far more easily than the other and would catch most of the frogs of that colour.

Look at the picture on the left (A). Can you guess which colour of frog was easier for the storks to spot? Which variety of frog has increased in number as a result of this natural selection? Colour in the picture on the right (B) to confirm your theory.

B

Q: What do you call a girl with a frog on her head?
A: Lily

Imaginary Animals

Invent an animal of your own and give it five distinctive characteristics.

Write each characteristic down and also think how it might help the animal to survive in a warm environment like the jungle. For example:

1. Ears (big, small, round, pointy)
2. Fur (coloured, patterned, short, long)
3. Tail (long, short, none at all)
4. Teeth (sharp, flat, toothless)
5. Legs (hooves, paws, long, short)

 Draw your animal and give it a unique name!

Draw your imaginary animal here.

CHARACTERISTICS

1. _____

2. _____

3. _____

4. _____

5. _____

Climate Change

Imagine there's a big change in the climate or environment, such as the weather becoming very cold for a long period of time, like an ice age. What would happen to your imaginary animal species?

Can you draw how natural selection over time might affect your animal's future generations? What adaptations or changes will enable this species to survive? (For example, they might grow longer fur to keep warm.)

NEW CHARACTERISTICS

1. _____

2. _____

3. _____

4. _____

5. _____

EVOLUTION BY NATURAL SELECTION

Under natural selection, organisms slowly change and adapt to their environment. Over thousands of years the differences add up and a species can change so much that they become a whole new species. Of course, just as new species form, others die out or become extinct.

✏ Match Extinct with Living Relatives

Look at the pictures of various animals below. The animals on the left are the ancestors, or share a close common ancestor, with the animals on the right (animals we see today). Can you match the extinct species with their living relatives by drawing a line between them?

Palaeomastodon

Hyracotherium

Smilodon

Samotherium

African elephant

Giraffe

Horse

Leopard

27

SCIENTIFIC NAMES

A genus is a group of closely related species that have descended from one common ancestor. The genus name and the species name together gives us the scientific name of an animal. For example, the lion belongs to the genus *Panthera,* and to the species *leo.* Its scientific name is *Panthera leo.* The name of the genus is written first, starting with a capital letter and the name of the species comes second.

> Genus + species = Scientific name

When scientists name a new species, they aren't allowed to name it after themselves, but they can name it after a friend. Sometimes scientists will pair up and promise to name their next species after each other!

Canis lupus

Related species ___2, 8, 10___

Panthera leo

Related species _____

Equus ferus

Related species _____

Mustela nivalis

Related species _____

Find the Relatives

Here are pictures of various animals with their scientific names. The animals on the left are looking to see if they can find any of their relatives in the 12 boxes below.

Look for animals with the same genus name and write their number next to 'Related species'. The first one has been done for you. Don't forget you can colour them in, too!

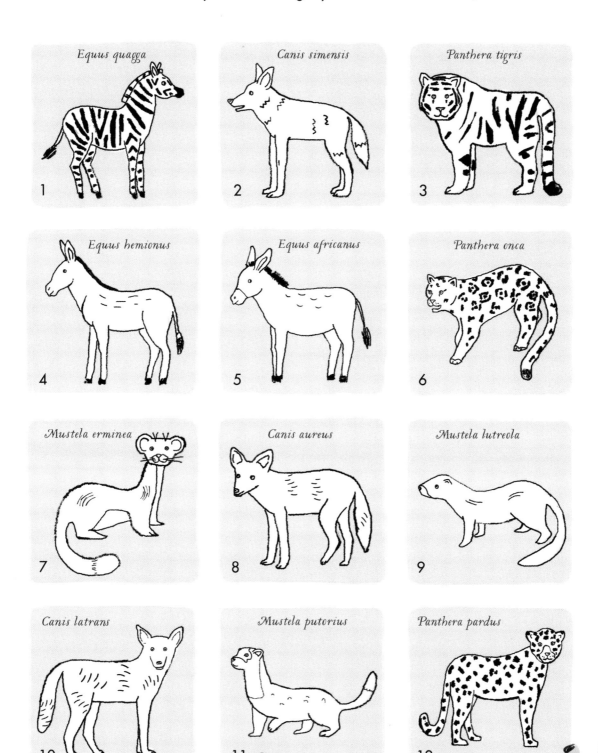

Equus quagga	*Canis simensis*	*Panthera tigris*
1	2	3
Equus hemionus	*Equus africanus*	*Panthera onca*
4	5	6
Mustela erminea	*Canis aureus*	*Mustela lutreola*
7	8	9
Canis latrans	*Mustela putorius*	*Panthera pardus*
10	11	12

GENUS EQUUS

Genus Equus is a group of closely related mammals. It included horses, asses and zebras. All these species evolved from one common ancestor. The earliest horse-like animals were called Hyracotherium – tiny creatures the size of a dog that lived 56 million years ago.

Name Your Own Dinosaur

Usually, the genus name of a dinosaur is made of two parts. Tyrannosaurus, for example, is made up of *tyranno* (tyrant) and *saurus* (lizard). To make the full scientific name you also need to add the species name – *Tyrannosaurus rex*. In the three columns below you will find words and their meanings.

1. Take one word from each column (A, B and C) to make your own dinosaur name.

2. Next, draw the dinosaur according to its name (for example, if you name it Ceratosaurus, it must have horns).

3. Try searching the internet to find out if it ever existed.

A. Genus name, first part

Avi – bird
Brachy – short
Deino – horrible
Draco – dragon
Mega or *Megalo* – big
Micro – small
Cerato – with horns
Ornitho – bird
Stego – with armour
Struthio – ostrich
Tyranno – tyrant

B. Genus name, second part

dromeus – runner
saurus – lizard
therium – beast
don – tooth
onyx – claw
raptor – kidnapper or thief
suchus – crocodile
pteryx – wing
ceratops – horn
titan – giant
venator – hunter

C. Species name

agilis – agile
altus – tall
crassus – solid
fortis – mighty
giganticus – giant
gracilis – slender
mirus – wonderful
parvus – small
rex – king
robustus – robust
rufus – red

Aviceratops fortis

Draw your dinosaur here.

Dinosaur name: _____

Q: What do you call two dinosaurs that have been in an accident?
A: Tyrannosaurus wrecks.

FOSSILS

Much of what we know about evolution comes from fossils. Fossils are the remains or impressions of plants and animals and are usually found in sedimentary rocks (rocks that have formed from layers of compacted sediment). The layers at the bottom contain older fossils and the layers closer to the top contain newer fossils. When we do find fossils, they can show us how animals and plants evolved over time.

NEWEST
ROCKS

TIME

OLDEST
ROCKS

Find the Missing Fossils

A geologist explores a mountain and finds several layers of rock with fossils in. In layers 2, 4 and 6 the fossils have fallen away from the rock. Looking at pictures A, B and C, can you guess which fossils belonged to which layer? Which layer is the oldest? How do you know?

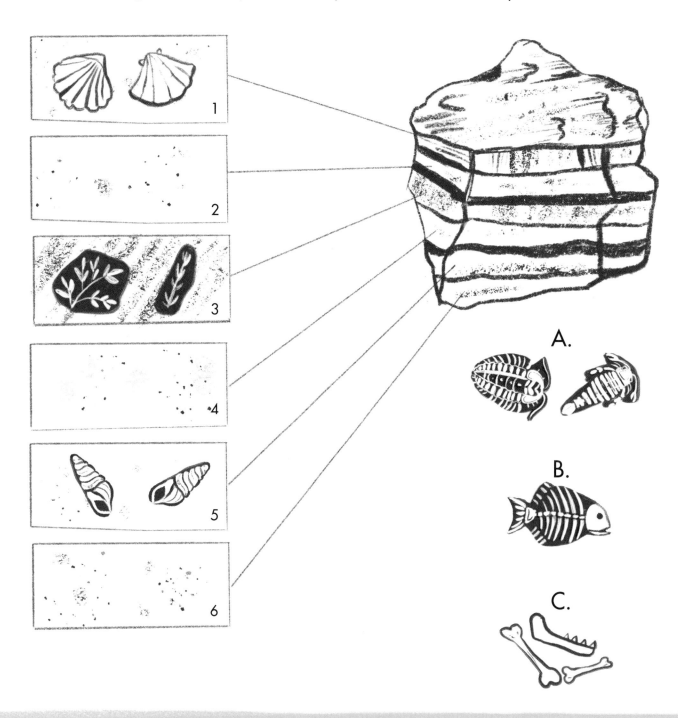

1

2

3

4

5

6

A.

B.

C.

 Q: What do you call a fossil that doesn't like to work? A: Lazybones.

35

EVOLUTIONARY TREES

Scientists often use diagrams that look like a tree to explain how species are related. The base of each branch represents a common ancestor and the tips of the branches are the descendants. These are very similar to family trees. Maybe you have a family tree in your home? You and your brothers and sisters (if you have any) are linked to your parents (they are your common ancestors). And you are related to your cousins, aunts and uncles by shared grandparents.

Cousin   Cousin   You   Sibling

Family Tree

Aunt   Parent

Grandparent

Complete the Evolutionary Tree

Look at the animals and think about which ones are more closely related.
Can you complete the evolutionary tree?

Panthera pardus
Leopard

Lutra lutra
Eurasian otter

Canis lupus
Wolf

Taxidea taxus
American badger

Canis latrans
Coyote

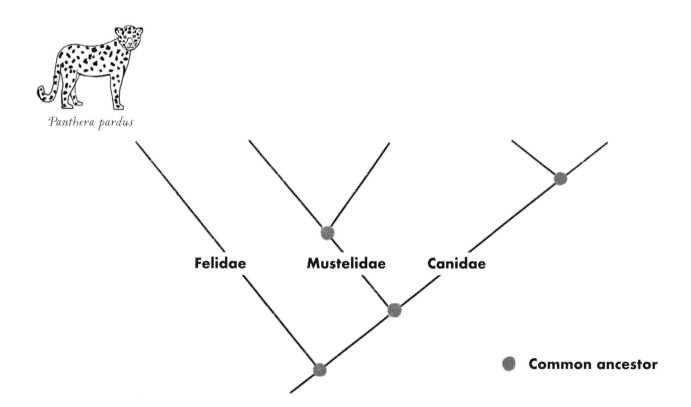

Panthera pardus

Felidae   **Mustelidae**   **Canidae**

● **Common ancestor**

Felidae – cat family
Canidae – dog-like carnivores
Mustelidae – badgers, otters, weasels and relatives

TREE OF LIFE

The tree of life is a diagram that shows the relationships between organisms, both living and extinct. The British naturalist Charles Darwin first used the term in his book *On the Origin of Species*. Scientists have since developed the evolutionary tree diagram to show how all life forms on this planet are related to one another.

FIVE-FINGERED LIMBS

Many animals have a very similar bone structure, even though their limbs look and function differently on the outside. This is known as the five-fingered bone structure. Animals such as lizards, birds, dogs and even humans have the same types of bones in the same order within their arms. This shows that many vertebrates (animals with a spine) are related, and share common ancestors.

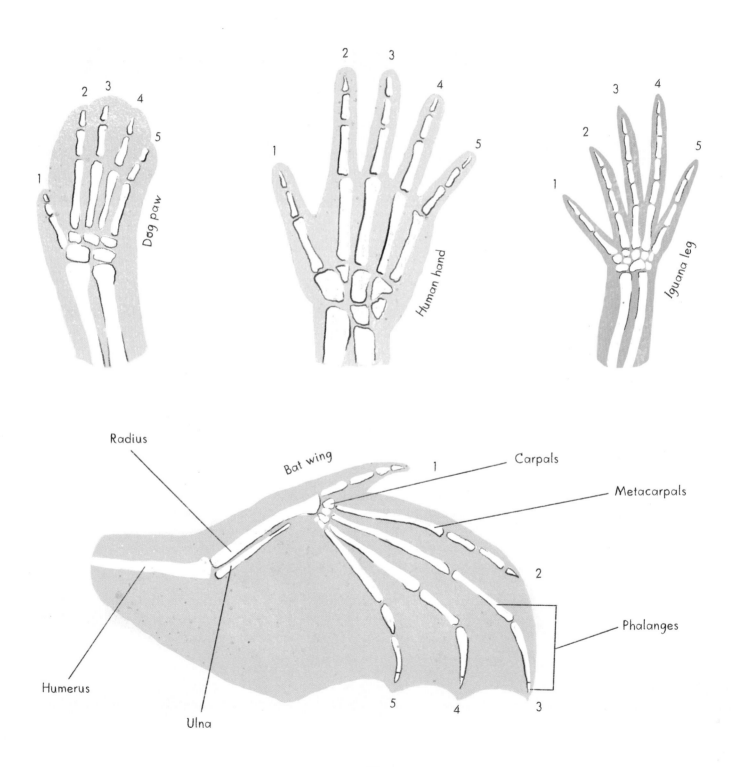

Colour the Bones

Here are the arm bones of five different animals. They all have the same type of bones in the same order. Can you colour the bones according to the key?

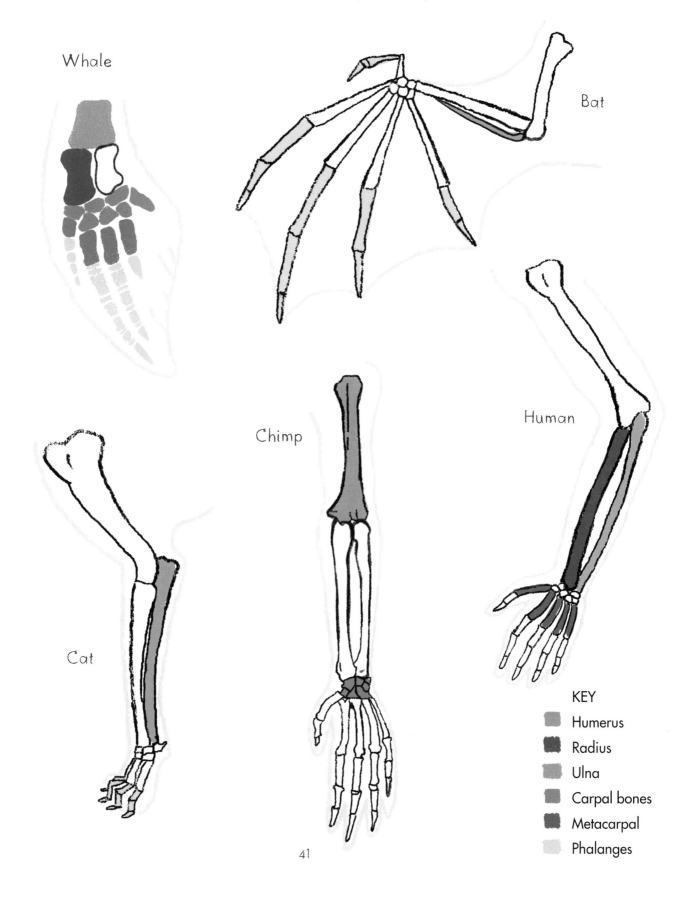

Whale

Bat

Human

Chimp

Cat

KEY

- Humerus
- Radius
- Ulna
- Carpal bones
- Metacarpal
- Phalanges

INSTINCT

Instinct is the way an animal is born knowing how to work with its environment. For example, many birds somehow know they must travel to warmer places during winter, and many bees create perfect hexagon shapes in which to store their honey, without ever being taught.

MIGRATION

In nature, animals may move from place to place, in order to find food or to escape dangers and problems. This is called migration. Because species migrate, they are eventually able to spread over long distances from where they originated. In their new environment species adapt and change even more.

Can you name the species that makes the world's longest migration? Hint: this bird flies 90,000 kilometres (56,000 miles) from pole to pole every year. You can search the internet for the answer with the help of an grown-up.

Solve the Maze

A group of wild horses is looking for new grazing pastures. Can you help them find their way through the maze of problems and perils, and into the grassy meadow?

Mountains, rivers and seas create natural barriers to migration, and many animals have difficulty crossing oceans.

Evolutionary Words

So far we've learned lots of different terms. Can you use the clues to complete the crossword?
You can look back through the book to find the answers!

Clues:

1. A favourable characteristic that helps an organism survive. (Down)
2. A group of similar-looking individuals that are able to reproduce. (Down)
3. Differences between animals or plants of the same species. (Across)
4. A group of closely related species that have descended from one common ancestor. (Across)
5. The remains or impressions of plants and animals trapped inside rock. (Across)

MICROBES

Microbes are very tiny organisms that can feed on pretty much anything. They can live almost anywhere, from the North Pole to the tip of your nose. By studying the DNA of living creatures, scientists have now realized that microbes vary a lot more than we once thought, and actually divide into two groups – Bacteria and Archaea. They might be small but, between them, bacteria and archaea have more species than animals, plants and fungi combined!

✏️ Colour in the Different Microbes
Colour the microbes in the petri dish below.

OBSERVATIONS USING A NATURE JOURNAL

Now that you have completed this activity book, you are well on the way to becoming a naturalist! One of the most important things a naturalist can have is a journal. For your journal, you can use a notebook with blank pages.

The best type of notebook has hard covers. You will need those covers for support because in nature there are not many desks for writing on. Also, a hardcover book will protect your notes from the elements. If you can, use a journal with an elastic band attachment to keep it closed whenever you're not using it. The elastic band prevents it from opening accidentally when dropped, which can be very helpful in wet or muddy conditions.

What to write or draw with

Pencils make the best drawing and writing tools for your journal. They are resistant to most weather conditions, rarely run out or wash away, and can write at any angle – unlike some ink pens.

What to write in your journal

Before you start your observations, always write down the date, time of day and your location. When recording your findings try to use descriptive words and all your senses, except taste! You can write down any questions for further research at home.

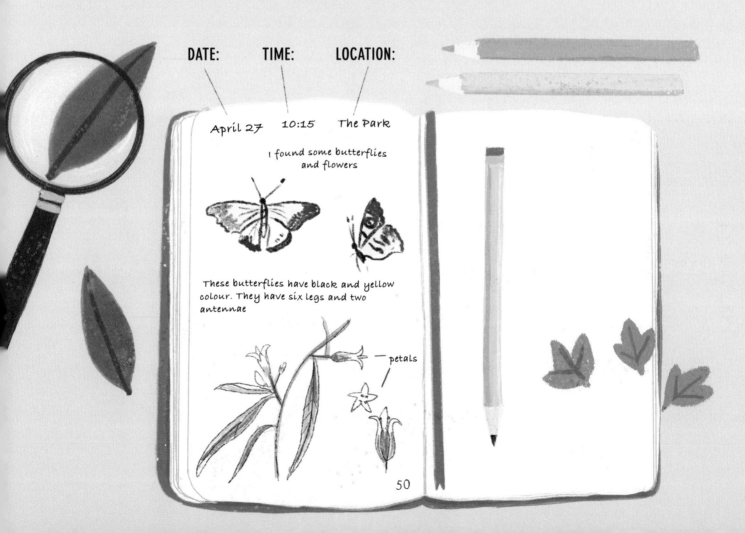

DATE: TIME: LOCATION:

April 27   10:15   The Park

I found some butterflies and flowers

These butterflies have black and yellow colour. They have six legs and two antennae

petals

50

Take your notebook on a visit to your nearest wildlife park or zoo. See if you can find any species of animals and insects that use camouflage to blend in with their environment in order to hide from predators or hunt. Make a note of the animal names and any other interesting details, and make a sketch, too. (A good example would be a chameleon, which changes colour to blend with its surroundings.)

At the zoo, on a farm, or in animal documentaries, you may have noticed some species and varieties of birds that cannot fly. All living species of birds have wings, but some have evolved in a way that they don't use them for flying any more. Are their wings useful in other ways? Can you name some flightless birds?

 You don't always have to travel somewhere special in order to record interesting observations in your nature journal. You can study farm animals, pets, and even the wildlife in your own garden or local park.

When you spot an animal record your observations.

- What does it eat?
- Where does it live?
- Does it interact with people or other animals?
- How does it get around (fly, walk, swim, slither)?
- Does it have any peculiarities, or things you don't understand? For example, does it like hoarding objects?

These are just a few questions to help you get started with your observations.

Even tiny insects like ants can be very interesting to study. Go to your garden, or local parks and woodland, to look for ants. Follow them to see where they come from and to find their home. Is it an anthill, or do they live at the base of a tree? In your notebook make a map of the areas where they nest.

In your observation notes you could write answers to these questions:
- Are they black, brown, reddish or yellow?
- What size are they?
- Are there ants of different colours and sizes in the same nest?
- Are there winged ants?
- Are there any other insects living with the ants?

If you find a nest where there are ants of varying colours or sizes, mark it for observation in your journal. Which colour and size of ant is more common? Do they act differently? If so, how?

You can also study ants to record their interactions with other insects, like aphids. Do they fight other insects or other ants? Do they communicate with their fellow ants? Do they have trails they follow, or do they wander around randomly?

Sometimes you will find an individual ant that has wandered away from its colony. You can follow a lone ant to see where it goes, and how far. You can even mark its trail on an ant map. Perhaps it is seeking something sweet, or perhaps the ant is on an observational mission of its own.

ANSWERS

5 The Theory of Evolution
Tyrannosaurus rex.

6 Organize in Groups

Insects

Mammal

7 Art Variations.
All sketches of the lizard will have small differences and will demonstrate variations.

10 Pigeon Breeds.
Pigeons are: 1, 4, 5, 6, 9, 14, 15.

11 Spot the Subtle Differences.
Identical are g, n, p.

14 Compare and Match
Matched 2–A, 5–B, 1–C, 3–D, 4–E. The tallest giraffe is number 4, and it will survive if all the short trees disappear.

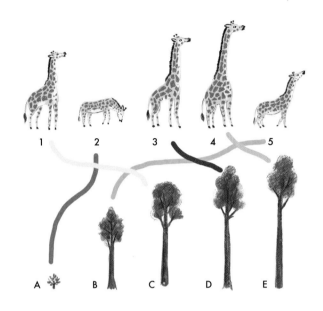

15 Camouflage
The habitat numbers in order top left to right – 3, 4, 3, 5, 5, 1, 4, 2, 1.

19 Find All the Moths.
There are 15 moths in total.

22–23 Frog Pond.
The light green frogs are easier to spot by the stork and get eaten more often. As a result, the dark green frogs survive, reproduce better and increase in numbers.

24 Imaginary Animals
Example animal could have the following characteristics:
1. large and round ears; 2. spotted grey fur; 3. long tail;
4. sharp teeth; 5. paws. Some characteristics that help animals survive in a warm climate and jungle are: camouflage; long and robust limbs to help climb trees; short fur to help with heat, poison or other deterrents.

25 Climate Change
Adaptations can include: thick layers of fat and fur for insulation against the cold; a greasy coat that sheds water after swimming; large furry feet to distribute their load and increase grip on the ice.

26-27 Match Ancestors with Descendants

Palaeomastodon – African elephant
Hyracotherium – Horse
Smilodon – Leopard
Samotherium – Giraffe

28-29 Find the Relatives

Canis lupus – 2, 8,10; *Panthera leo* – 3, 6,12;
Equus ferus – 1, 4, 5; *Mustela nivalis* – 7, 9,11.

32-33 Name Your Own Dinosaur. Example name:

Aviceratops fortis. It will have feathers (*avi* – bird),
a horn (*ceratops* – horn) and will be formidable
(*fortis* – mighty).

35 Find the Missing Fossils

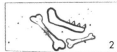

2 – C.

4 – B.

6 – A.

The oldest is layer 6
because it was the one on
the bottom of the rock.

37 Complete the Evolutionary Tree

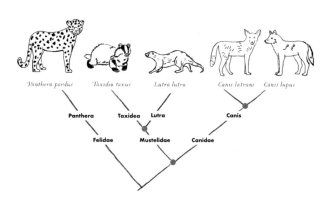

41 Colour the Bones

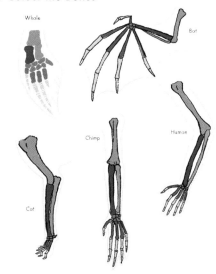

44 Migration. The arctic tern makes the world's longest migration.

45 Solve the Maze

48 Evolutionary Words

With huge thanks to all my collaborators!

Science help: Lia Stelea, Dr Claire Asher and Dr Nick Crumpton

Editing: Anna Barnes Robinson

Layout and design: Keren Greenfeld

Other help and support: Tamara Forge, Veronique Baxter,
the wider team at Penguin Random House, my family and friends!

PUFFIN BOOKS

UK | USA | Canada | Ireland | Australia
India | New Zealand | South Africa

Puffin Books is part of the Penguin Random House group of companies
whose addresses can be found at global.penguinrandomhouse.com.

Penguin
Random House
UK

First published 2020
001

Printed in Latvia
A CIP catalogue record for this book is available from the British Library

ISBN: 978–0–241–44619–5

All correspondence to:
Puffin Books, Penguin Random House Children's
One Embassy Gardens, 8 Viaduct Gardens, London SW11 7BW

MIX
Paper from
responsible sources
FSC® C018179